SPY WITH THE MISSING BRAIN

Written by Ken Ross
Illustrated by Barry Green

HENDERSON
PUBLISHING PLC

©1993 HENDERSON PUBLISHING PLC

Doctor Rotcod peered through the sights on his Superscan XB11. Sweat poured down his forehead and trickled off the end of his nose. 'I don't believe it...' he gasped, then he fainted.

'Wake up, Rotcod!' shouted Spy Chief Z. 'I must know what has happened to H-Two-O.'

A nurse placed a dampened cloth across the doctor's face. In a few moments he stirred. His eyes opened widely, and he turned to look at the spy chief.

'There's nothing inside his head,' murmured Doctor Rotcod, 'H-Two-O's brain is missing.' 'Missing?' repeated Spy Chief Z in amazement. 'Do you realise what might happen if the contents of H-Two-O's brain falls into enemy hands?'

An emergency alarm sounded throughout Spy HQ. The country's best spy was called to duty, then briefed on the secret contents of H-Two-O's missing brain. Among the information were the codenames of spies hiding in foreign cities. Can you work out in which cities these spies were working?

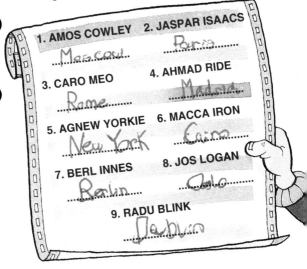

1. AMOS COWLEY

Moscow

2. JASPAR ISAACS

Paris

3. CARO MEO

Rome

4. AHMAD RIDE

Madrid

5. AGNEW YORKIE

New York

6. MACCA IRON

Cairo

7. BERL INNES

Berlin

8. JOS LOGAN

Oslo

9. RADU BLINK

Dublin

Master Spy H-Three-O was given one hour in which to trace the final movements of H-Two-O. As far as anyone knew, H-Two-O had not left Spy HQ, so there was a good chance that those who had stolen the brain were still inside the building.

'I shall tell the Prime Minister,' said Spy Chief Z. 'Good luck, H-Three-O. The future of our country depends on you.'

ANSWERS ON PAGE 24

H-Three-O powered up his booster boots and shot off to the staff canteen on floor ten. It was here H-Two-O had been found by the cook, and it was possibly here where the theft of the brain took place.

The cook remembered that H-Two-O had won a pair of pot ducks at the All Spies Bingo Evening. He'd looked particularly pleased, and he'd been sharing a joke with another man.

Which was the last-number H-Two-O marked on his card?

'Did you recognise this other man?' asked H-Three-O.
'Never seen him before,' said Cook, 'but he looked like a pickled gherkin.'

H-Three-O was still questioning the cook when he was summoned to the ground floor. The Prime Minister had arrived at Spy HQ and he was insisting on an up-to-the-minute report.

Inside Spy Chief Z's office the bookshelves and tables were shaking with the sound of the PM's voice.

'This country has aeroplanes in the skies, has ships on the seas, has tanks on land, has one million fighting men, and you lose a brain!' he blasted.

'H-Three-O, sir,' said the Master Spy after he'd knocked and entered. There was a long silence.

Can you pair up these?

ARMY	AERO-PLANES	NAVY	TANKS	AIRFORCE	SHIPS

At last the Prime Minister spoke. News of the missing brain must not reach the public. No-one who didn't already know of its disappearance must find out.

HOW MANY PEOPLE ALREADY KNEW?

The Prime Minister continued, 'I must impress on you that your fellow spy's brain holds the passwords to every Top Secret computer in the government building. Each password reads in order Z-A and then from 9-1. If the brain is not found, we shall never gain access to the computer's memories again. You must find that brain!'

Can you rearrange the passwords?

Computer 1: TJFQS-43763

Computer 2: FUOWR-56273

Computer 3: NOKRA-14239

Computer 4: NZXEV-36279

Computer 5: HITDM-47283

Computer 6: LEKGA-14286

'I can assure you, Sir, the missing brain will be found,' said H-Three-O. He left Spy Chief Z's office and looked up at the ten floors above him. Where was the most likely place to find the brain?

H-Three-O again blasted off on his booster boots and landed on floor nine of Spy HQ. He met Professor Decoder who was working on a new code.

'This code depends on pairs,' said the Prof. 'If you have two A's in the message, you cross them out, and if you have two b's you cross them out also. Pairs, do you see?'

'Yes,' replied H-Two-O, 'but all I need to know is whether you have a man who looks like a pickled gherkin working in your Decoding Department.'

The Prof. took a piece of paper and wrote down his answer to H-Three-O's question.
It read:

WE SAW
WISE LIDS
WASH LEGS.
DID DIGS
EAT? NO
HE ATE

It took H-Three-O less than fifteen seconds to work out the answer before he parachuted to floor seven. Can you find the reply quicker than H-Three-O?

In floor seven's Foreign Affairs Department some apprentice spies were actually in tears when they'd heard about H-Two-O's missing brain. H-Two-O was a popular guy here, and even though the brain's theft was supposed to be kept secret, everyone was openly talking about it.

'We're going to offer a reward,' said one apprentice.

'We've collected 200 dollars, 500 yen and 390 francs,' said another apprentice.

DO YOU KNOW WHICH COUNTRIES HAVE THESE CURRENCIES?

DOLLARS .... YEN .... FRANCS ....

'I need to know what you heard and saw before and after the sad event,' said H-Three-O to the young helpful spies.

He was told of a pungent smell coming down from floor ten. He was told of a strange mist. And they all agreed there'd been something like a mini-earthquake.

H-Three-O checked the readings on his Wobble Status Instrument, and sure enough, at the time of H-Two-O's unfortunate meeting with a brain thief, there had been some kind of earthquake. He was temporarily puzzled. There hadn't been a notable earthquake in this country for centuries.

MEANWHILE...

'Let's look at the evidence,' said Spy Chief Z.

'The brain is missing, we can't see it,' said Doctor Rotcod.

'Oh,' said Spy Chief Z.

'Pea,' said Doctor Rotcod.

'Queue,' said Spy Chief Z.

'Are we getting anywhere?' enquired Doctor Rotcod.

'S-pose not,' said Spy Chief Z.

They had a cup of tea and a game of I-Spy instead.

'You go first,' said Rotcod.

Can you make up a conversation using words that sound like letters? Here are some words to get you started:

HAY BE BEE SEE SEA HE GEE EYE JAY KAY HELL HEM HEN HO OH PEA QUEUE ARE TEA YOU EWE DOUBLE-YOU WHY ZED

H-Three-O decided to take to pieces the floor below the Foreign Affairs Department. The offices here weren't used, so no-one would be moved from his workplace.

Floor six was made of slot-together plastic bricks. Once one brick was moved, the remainder were easily dislodged. H-Three-O had each brick inspected for traces of brain cells. If H-Two-O had been here, there would be evidence.

With only a few bricks to go, there was a huge jolt. Floor seven crashed down onto the top of floor five. Floor six vanished in a puff of smoke from H-Three-O's crushed rooster roots.

H-Three-O wasn't injured, only dazed. He looked up from the ground and saw the apprentice spies gazing down on him.

'That was just like what happened when H-Two-O's brain went missing,' they said.

So, thought H-Three-O, it could have been the building moving, or even an explosion. But why? And why no trace of the man who looked like a pickled gherkin?

CAN YOU SPOT THE DELIBERATE
MISTAKE ON THIS PAGE?

Before H-Three-O had time to think further, he was arrested by the Spy Security Robots that guarded Spy HQ every day and every night. They couldn't speak English, but they frisked him and placed him in handcuffs. He was then taken to Spy Chief Z's office on the ground floor.

Spy Chief Z looked angry. The Prime Minister looked even angrier.
'What's this about?' said H-Three-O, innocently.

'What's this about?' exclaimed the spy chief. 'You have almost demolished Spy HQ and you ask why you have been arrested!'

'Perhaps you took H-Two-O's brain,' said the Prime Minister. He looked at Spy Chief Z and nodded. They were going to put H-Three-O in jail.

If H-Three-O went to jail, he could always pass the time by counting his brain cells. How many has he (and everyone else) got?

(a) 24	(b) 296	(c) countless millions

H-Three-O ran away from the robots who were guarding the main door to Spy Chief Z's office. He ran along an open corridor to escape. Can you guide him first to the Gadget Shop, where he can cut off his handcuffs, then back to the central square of Spy HQ?

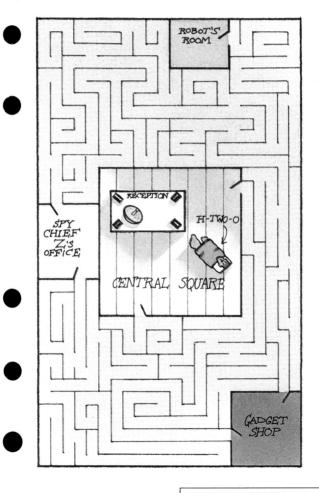

With a new pair of booster boots strapped to his feet, H-Three-O blasted off to the garden complex on floor three. To prove his innocence, he had to find the man who looked like a pickled gherkin.

The Head Gardener knew no such man, and neither did the wood carvers who shaped wood for use in the Gadget Shop.

To make matters even worse, Spy Security Robots were looking everywhere for H-Three-O. He had to disguise himself with some objects he found in a cardboard box inside the gardener's shed.

Which objects could H-Three-O choose to disguise his face?

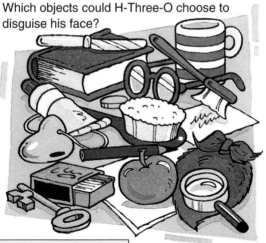

For over half an hour the emergency precaution bell rang out in Spy HQ. Even wearing his disguise, H-Three-O didn't dare to venture beyond the gardener's shed. He thought, then thought some more. Then he made up a rhyme that seemed very relevant to the case, and chalked it on the wall of the garden shed.

my first is in rib
but not in write
my second's in rig
but not in night
my third is in art
but not in trip
my fourth's in dirt
but not in clap
my last is in rain
but not in straight
my whole is for
          thinking
about H-Two-O's
              fate
    WHAT IS IT?

H-Three-O put the chalk in his pocket. Inside his pocket he found a handful of debris which must have fallen when floor six collapsed. In the debris was a tiny green flake of vegetable. It smelled of vinegar. This was a significant clue!

It was now over one hour since Doctor Rotcod's Superscan XB11 detected a space where H-Two-O's brain should have been. Throughout the country the crisis was causing problems for citizens.

Roadblocks had been set up around the capital. Airport security was tightened in fear that the brain would be smuggled out to a foreign country.

Policemen on foot patrol were inspecting shopping bags, boxes, car boots, and anywhere a brain could be hidden.

The policy to keep the missing brain a secret hadn't worked. Even national television had special bulletins to report the investigation's progress.

Can you think of anything else that might be done to trace the missing brain?

....

> WHAT DO YOU CALL A SPY
> WITH EIGHT LEGS?

Still wearing his disguise, H-Three-O crept from the gardener's shed and wandered a little way around the garden complex. All but one or two Spy Security Robots had gone back to their base on the ground floor. Daringly, H-Three-O pushed back the shutters on a large room which was marked 'GROWING CELL'. The shutters made a clanging noise, but no-one came to investigate. Inside the room, the master spy found huge plant pots neatly arranged in lines. Each plant pot was as high as his chin. Something unusual was growing here.

Can you guess what was growing in the plant pots?

From floor three, H-Three-O climbed up a ventilation shaft, all the way up to the Foreign Affairs Department, or what was left of it after the earthquake-cum-explosion.

There was a host of people gathered there, among them Spy Chief Z and the Prime Minister. The Superintendent of Robots was issuing orders on his intercom. Other officials were calling for H-Three-O to be put on trial for crimes against the state. Even a few apprentice spies were now convinced that H-Three-O had stolen H-Two-O's brain.

'He's the only person in the building to come under suspicion,' said Spy Chief Z.

'He escaped from my Robots,' said the Superintendent.

H-Three-O leapt from the vent, tore off his disguise, and gave the assembly a huge shock. 'I'll give you three good reasons why it was not me who stole the brain, if you'll give me three or four minutes to prove where the brain is now,' he said.

Everyone was speechless. H-Three-O gave his three reasons why he had not stolen the brain. Do you know which they were?

Reason 1: He was with Doctor Rotcod when the discovery of the missing brain was made.

Reason 2: The cook had seen H-Two-O with another man in the canteen on floor ten. She was the last person to see H-Two-O with his brain.

Reason 3: H-Two-O had never had a brain, so it couldn't have been stolen.

Reason 4: The apprentice spies had said there was a pungent smell, a strange mist, and a loud crash about the same time as the brain disappeared.

Reason 5: The tiny green flake he had found in the debris proved that the brain had not fallen into enemy hands.

At least the Prime Minister was convinced that there was cause to doubt the guilt of H-Three-O.

'You have a few minutes to prove your case,' he said.

'That's all I'll need', replied H-Three-O.

Escorted by six powerful Spy Security Robots, H-Three-O parachuted down to the Diet Workshop on floor four. There were only two more facts he needed to establish before he could safely prove what had happened to H-Two-O's missing brain.

Miss Bone, the workshop's slimming expert, could clear up the first area of doubt. He found her teaching exercise techniques to three spies who, in total, weighed 320 kilograms.

'Charlie weighs one and a half times more than Fred,' said Miss Bone, 'and Albert weighs the same as Charlie. None of the spies weighs 60, 100, or 140 kilograms, so how much does each spy weigh?'

DO YOU KNOW?
H-THREE-O ANSWERED IMMEDIATELY.

CHARLIE ....kg   ALBERT ....kg   FRED ......kg

'Now here is a question for you, Miss Bone,' said H-Three-O, hoping he already knew the answer. 'What does a good, healthy spy eat?'

Miss Bone stood back on her heels and put her hands firmly on her hips. 'No doubt about it,' she said, 'a good, healthy spy eats big juicy delicious chunky polished pure super snappy hunky wowee crunchy muscular vegetables. Show me a perfect vegetable and I will show you a perfect spy.'

'That's a matter of opinion,' said H-Three-O. He pondered for a moment and walked between two of the towering robots who'd never taken their sight devices off him. 'Now tell me if you will, Miss Bone.... Did you tell H-Two-O that he should eat big juicy delicious polished pure super snappy hunky wowee crunchy muscular vegetables?'

'I most certainly did,' she answered.

'Then the mystery is almost solved,' said H-Three-O with a smile on his face.

H-Three-O once more loosened his parachute as he descended to the ground floor. He landed in the centre of all those who'd gathered to see him taken off to prison.

'Here, make fools of yourselves,' he said, handing out a form to each accuser. They took out their pens and made their guesses.

> YOUR BIG CHANCE
> WHAT HAPPENED TO H-TWO-O'S BRAIN?

Report by:

....

(Spy CODE NAME)

The Prime Minister and senior staff members formed a semi-circle around H-Two-O who was now strapped to a Rocket Spin Z46 in the middle of Spy HQ's ground floor square.

H-Three-O brought them to silence. 'Observe,' he said, pointing to H-Two-O's swollen foot. 'Our friend was last seen by the cook in the staff canteen. He was with a man who looked like a pickled gherkin...'

'He was,' confirmed the cook.

'Not so,' said H-Three-O, 'he was actually with a man-size pickled gherkin which had been grown in the growing cell in the garden complex.'

'My special vegetables!' shouted Miss Bone.

'Precisely,' said H-Three-O. 'H-Two-O ate the man-size gherkin... and then he belched. The backwind of the belch not only caused the earthquake, but it also rocketed his brain to his own foot.'

H-Three-O switched on the Rocket Spin Z46. Very soon H-Two-O's brain was back inside his head. 'You saved my life,' said H-Two-O gratefully.

'You've saved our country,' said a humbled Prime Minister.

'All part of the job,' said a modest H-Three-O, shoving away the unfriendly Spy Security Robots.

ANSWERS

page 3
1. Moscow, 2. Paris,
3. Rome, 4. Madrid,
5. New York, 6. Cairo, 7.
Berlin, 8. Oslo, 9. Dublin

page 4
Number 22
Twenty two is called out
as 'two little ducks' when
playing bingo

page 5
Army/Tanks,
Airforce/Aeroplanes,
Navy/Ships

page 6
7 at most. H-Three-O, Spy
Chief Z, Prime Minister,
Doctor Rotcod, his nurse,
possibly the cook, and the
man who looked like a
pickled gherkin.

Passwords
1. TSQJF-76433
2. WUROF-76532
3. RONKA-94321
4. ZXVNE-97632
5. TMIHD-87432
6. LKGEA-86421

page 8
No. If you cross out all the
duplications, you're left
with...no.

page 9
Dollars/USA
Yen/Japan
Francs/France

page 11
Rooster roots should read
booster boots

page 12
(c) countless millions

page 13

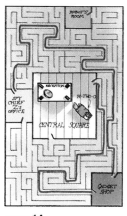

page 14
The false nose
and spectacles.

page 15
Brain

page 16
A spy-der (spider)

page 17
Huge vegetables

page 19
Reasons 2, 4 and 5

page 20
Charlie and Albert
both weigh 120k,
Fred weighs 80k.